HOUGHTON MIFFLIN

Reading

A Legacy of Literacy

Here We Go!

Senior Authors
J. David Cooper
John J. Pikulski

Authors
Patricia A. Ackerman
Kathryn H. Au
David J. Chard
Gilbert G. Garcia
Claude N. Goldenberg
Marjorie Y. Lipson
Susan E. Page
Shane Templeton
Sheila W. Valencia
MaryEllen Vogt

Consultants
Linda H. Butler
Linnea C. Ehri
Carla B. Ford

 HOUGHTON MIFFLIN   BOSTON • MORRIS PLAINS, NJ

California • Colorado • Georgia • Illinois • New Jersey • Texas

Cover and title page photography by Michelle Joyce.

Cover illustration by Nadine Bernard Westcott.

Acknowledgments begin on page 256.

Printed in the U.S.A.

ISBN: 0-618-15668-2

789-DW-06 05 04

All Together Now 12

Big Book: Ten Dogs in the Window
by Claire Masurel
illustrated by Pamela Paparone
Bank Street College Best Children's
Books of the Year

realistic
fiction

realistic fiction

nonfiction

Phonics Library:
Nan Cat
Fat Cat
Tan Fan

On My Way Practice Readers

Cat
by Alice Lisson

Fan Cat Can Jump
by Iris Littleman

One Big Hit
by Kathryn Lewis

Theme Paperbacks

Bear Play
by Miela Ford

Dan and Dan
by Marcia Leonard
photographs by
Dorothy Handelman

I Had a Hippopotamus
by Hector Viveros Lee

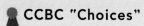 CCBC "Choices"

Surprise! 128

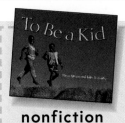

Big Book: Minerva Louise at School
by Janet Morgan Stoeke

🎗 IRA/CBC Children's Choice
Bank Street College Best Children's
Books of the Year

fantasy

**Phonics Library:
Not Yet!
Big Ben
Get Wet, Ken!**

Not Yet!
by Sid Jones
illustrated by Kelly Murphy

Len Hen can get one
kit in the tan van.

fantasy

Big Book: Jasper's Beanstalk
by Nick Butterworth and Mick Inkpen

🎗 Best Books for Children
United Kingdom Children's Book Award

Phonics Library:
The Bug Kit
Quit It, Zig!
Rug Tug

9

On My Way Practice Readers

Five Big Boxes
by Irma Singer

The Pet
by Maria Cara

Where Is Tug Bug?
by Oscar Gake

Theme Paperbacks

"What Is That?" Said the Cat
by Grace Maccarone
illustrated by Jeffrey Scherer

The Pet Vet
by Marcia Leonard
photographs by
Dorothy Handelman

Spots
by Marcia Leonard
photographs by
Dorothy Handelman

For suggestions of other good books, go to

www.calvertschool.org/goodbooks.

®

Dear Calvert Family,

Calvert School respects the privacy of our students and families and does not share information about families with other companies or organizations. This book contains a reference to a Web site that requires registration. The sponsor of the site gathers personal information for marketing purposes. We do not feel this is appropriate content in a textbook.

Please contact us if you have any concerns or questions.

10713 Gilroy Road • Suite B • Hunt Valley, MD 21031 • www.calvertschool.org
inquiry@calvertservices.org • 888.487.4652 • 410-785-3400 • 410-785-3418 (fax)

All Together Now

Because we do
All things together
All things improve,
Even weather.

**from the poem
"Together"
by Paul Engle**

The Cat Sat

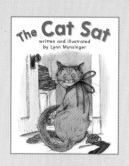

Words to Know

go   cat
on   mat
the   sat

The cat sat on the mat.

Go, cat.

Meet the Author and Illustrator
Lynn Munsinger

16

The Cat Sat

written and illustrated
by Lynn Munsinger

The cat sat on the basket.

Go, cat!

The cat sat on the table.

Go, cat!

The cat sat on the TV.

Go, cat!

The cat sat on Pam.

Think About the Story

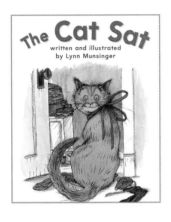

1 Why did the girl say, "Go, cat"?

2 What was the best place for the cat to sit?

3 How would you get the cat to move?

Write a Label

Draw and label a picture of the cat. Share your picture.

27

The Mat

The Mat
by Nadine Bernard Westcott

Words to Know

go	cat
on	mat
the	sat

Cat sat.

Cat sat on the mat.

Go, Cat!

29

Meet the
Author and Illustrator
Nadine Bernard Westcott

30

The Mat

by Nadine Bernard Westcott

The cat sat on the mat.

33

Go, cat, go!

The cow sat on the mat.

The goat sat on the cow.

The dog sat on the cow.

38

The cat sat on the dog.

Go, cow, go!

The mat sat on the cat.

Think About the Story

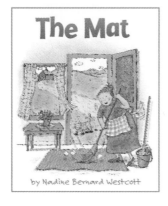

The Mat
by Nadine Bernard Westcott

1 Why do you think the animals sat on the mat?

2 Why did the woman yell, "Go"?

3 Would you want animals in your house? Why?

Write a Sign

Make a sign to help keep
the animals out of the house.

45

Cats

Cats are furry, cats are small
Cats are hardly big at all
Cats can purr and cats can mew
Do you like cats?
I sure do!

by Jacquiline Kirk, Age 9
Mauritius, Indian Ocean

46

At Night

When night is dark
my cat is wise
to light the lanterns
in his eyes.

by Aileen Fisher

Nan and Fan

illustrated by Lisa Campbell Ernst

Words to Know

not	Fan
jump	can
here	pat
and	fat
Nan	

Nan can jump.
Fan can not.

Nan and Fan can go here.

Nan can pat the fat cat.

Meet the Illustrator
Lisa Campbell Ernst

illustrated by Lisa Campbell Ernst

Nan can go with Mom.

Fan can not.

Nan can jump.

Fan can not.

Nan can pat the fat cat.

Fan can not.

Nan can go here.

Fan can not.

Fan, go with Mom!

Nan can go to school.

Fan can go with Mom.

Think About the Story

Nan and Fan
illustrated by Lisa Campbell Ernst

1 Why did Fan follow Nan?

2 Why can't Fan go to Nan's school?

3 What would you do if a pet followed you to school?

Writing

Write a List

Make a class list of pets. Write "Our Pets" at the top of the list.

written by Diane Hoyt-Goldsmith
photographs by Joel Benjamin

Words to Know

here	fan
we	Ann
and	Nat
too	Pat
can	

Ann can fan.

Ann and Pat can fan.

Nat can fan here, too.
We can fan!

Meet the Author

Diane Hoyt-Goldsmith

Meet the Photographer

Joel Benjamin

We Can!

written by Diane Hoyt-Goldsmith
photographs by Joel Benjamin

Here we go!

Ann can get on the bus.

Pat can get on the bus, too.

Ann can read at school.

Pat can read, too.

Ann can write at school.

Nat can write, too.

Ann can draw a fan at school.

Pat can draw a fan, too.

Nat can draw a fan, too.

Ann, Nat, and Pat can fan!

Think About the Story

written by Diane Hoyt-Goldsmith
photographs by Joel Benjamin

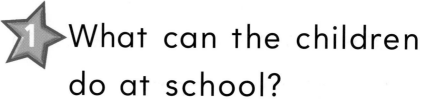
1 What can the children do at school?

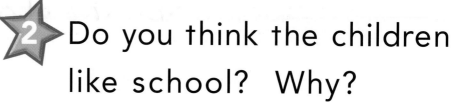
2 Do you think the children like school? Why?

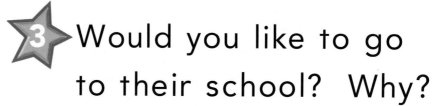
3 Would you like to go to their school? Why?

Describe a Character

Use punch-out letters to make a character's name. Then write one word to describe the character.

The More We Get Together

The more we get together,
  together, together,
The more we get together,
  the happier we'll be.
'Cause your friends are my friends,
  and my friends are your friends,
The more we get together,
  the happier we'll be.

Traditional

The Big Hit

written by
Angela Shelf Medearis

illustrated by
John Ceballos

Words to Know

who   big
find   hit
a   bat
have   ran
one

Who can find a big, big bat?

We have a big bat.

Nan can hit one hit.

Nan ran.

Meet the Author
Angela Shelf Medearis

Meet the Illustrator
John Ceballos

The Big Hit

written by
Angela Shelf Medearis

illustrated by
John Ceballos

Who can find a big bat?

We have a big bat.

Who can hit the ball?

We can hit the ball!

Nat hit the ball.
Nat hit a little hit.

Go, Nat, go!

Nat ran fast!

Nan hit the ball.
Nan hit a little hit.

Go, Nan, go!

Nan ran fast.

Pat hit the ball.
Pat hit one big hit!

We ran fast!

Think About the Story

The **Big Hit**
written by
Angela Shelf Medearis

illustrated by
John Ceballos

1 Do you think the children like to play ball? Why?

2 Why did the children chase the dog?

3 How would you get the ball from the dog?

Writing ▶

Write a Name

Draw your favorite character from the story. Write the character's name.

Words to Know

a	big
find	pig
have	fig
one	fit
who	sit
to	hat
	ran

Who can Big Pig find?
Go to Nan, Big Pig.

Big Pig ran.

Sit, Big Pig.
Have one big fat fig.

Can a hat fit Big Pig?

Meet the Author and Illustrator
David McPhail

Big Pig

by David McPhail

Chapter 1

Here is the farm.
What can we find at the farm?

We find a big hat at the farm.

Can the big hat fit Matt?
No, Matt is too little.

Can the big hat fit Nan?
No, Nan is too little.

Who can the big hat fit?

It can fit Big Pig!
Big Pig can have the big hat.

Chapter 2

1. Feed Big Pig.
2. Sit on Big Pig.

Who can feed Big Pig?
Who can sit on Big Pig?

Nan can feed Big Pig.
Nan can feed a fig to Big Pig.

Nan can sit on Big Pig.

Matt can feed Big Pig, too.
Big Pig can have one carrot.

Matt can sit on Big Pig with Nan.

Can Big Pig go?

Big Pig ran!
Matt and Nan sat!

Think About the Story

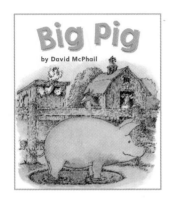

1 Why does Big Pig get the hat?

2 Why did Nan and Matt sit on Big Pig?

3 Would you like to visit Big Pig's farm? Why?

Writing ▶

Write a Menu

What does Big Pig like to eat?
Draw a picture and label it.

There Was a Small

There was a small pig who wept tears
When his mother said,
   "I'll wash your ears."
As she poured on the soap,
He cried, "Oh, how I hope
This won't happen again for ten years!"

by Arnold Lobel

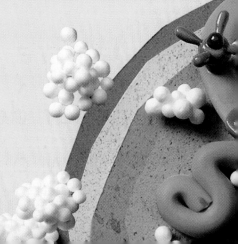

126

Pig Who Wept Tears

Surprise!

Read Together

No matter where
   I travel,
No matter where
   I roam,
No matter where
   I find myself,
I always am
   at home.

**from the poem "Riddle"
by Mary Ann Hoberman**

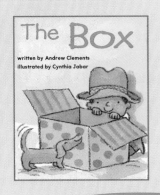

The Box

written by Andrew Clements
illustrated by Cynthia Jabar

Words to Know

in	Dot
once	got
what	lot
Dan	box
wig	fox

Once Dan and Dot got a big box. What can fit in the big box?

130

A wig can fit.
A fox can fit.

A lot can fit in the big box.

Meet the Author
Andrew Clements

Meet the Illustrator
Cynthia Jabar

The Box

written by Andrew Clements

illustrated by Cynthia Jabar

Once Dan got a big box.
What can Dan do with the box?

What can fit in the box?
Dan can fit a lot in the box.

A tan fox is little.
It can fit in the box.

A pig in a wig is little.
It can fit in the box.

A hat can fit in the box, too.
A lot can fit in the box.

What can Dan do with the box?

Dot got the box.

What can Dot find in the box?

Dot can find a little fox.

Dot can find a pig in a wig.

Dot can find a hat in the box.
Dot got a lot in the box!

Dan and Dot can fit in the box.
We can do a lot with a box!

145

Think About the Story

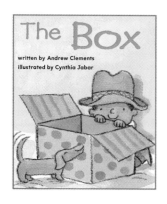

The Box
written by Andrew Clements
illustrated by Cynthia Jabar

1 How many things did Dan put in the box?

2 What might Dot do with the things in the box?

3 What would you put in the box?

Write a Description

Draw something you would put in the box. Write about your picture.

Words to Know

upon	wig
in	Dan
what	Dot
two	lot
three	box
four	Fox
five	Ox

A big box sat upon a mat.
What can we find in the box?

 Fox got wig one.

 Ox got wig two.

 Cat got wig three.

 Dot got wig four.

 Dan got wig five.

 What a lot in a big box!

Meet the Author and Illustrator
Valeria Petrone

Wigs in a Box

by Valeria Petrone

A big box sat upon a shelf.
Can Pat Pig win the box?

153

Pat Pig hit the ball in.
Pat Pig got the box!

A lot can fit in a big box.
What can Pat Pig find in here?

Pat Pig can find one wig.

One, two, three, four, five wigs!
What can Pat Pig do with five wigs?

Wig one can fit Pat Pig.
Here is a pig in a wig!

Wig two can fit Dot Fox.
Here is a fox in a wig!

Wig three can fit Dan Dog.
Here is a dog in a wig!

Wig four can fit Fat Cat.
Here is a cat in a wig!

Wig five can fit Tan Ox.
Here is an ox in a wig!

One, two, three, four, five wigs!
Thanks a lot, Pat Pig!

Think About the Story

1. What plan did Pat Pig make when he saw the wigs in the box?

2. Why did the animals thank Pat Pig?

3. Which wig would you choose?

Write a Character Description

Use punch-out letters to write your favorite character's name. Then write some words to tell about the character.

Here Is

Here is the beehive.
Where are the bees?

Hidden away where
nobody sees.

Watch and you'll
see them come
out of the hive.

the Beehive

One, two, three, four, five.

Bzzzzzzz ...
all fly away!

167

What Can a Vet Do?

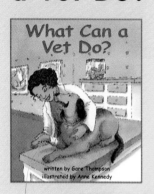

What Can a Vet Do?

written by Gare Thompson
illustrated by Anne Kennedy

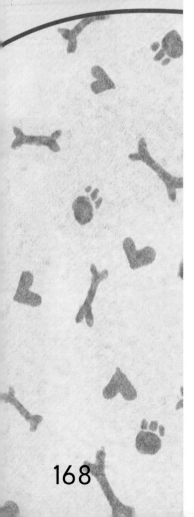

Words to Know

my	yet
do	pet
for	get
is	wet
kit	Ben
vet	pen

Ben is my pet.
Do not get wet, Ben.

Is Ben at the vet?
Not yet.

Get in the pen, Ben.
The vet can get a kit.
What can the vet do for Ben?

Meet the Author
Gare Thompson

Meet the Illustrator
Anne Kennedy

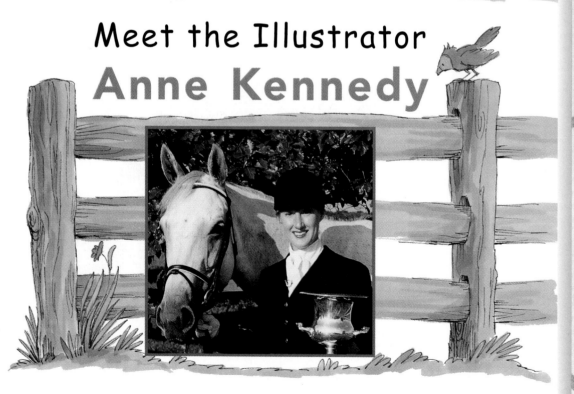

What Can a Vet Do?

written by Gare Thompson
illustrated by Anne Kennedy

Chapter 1

Big Ben is my pet cat.
What bit Big Ben?

My cat can go to the vet.
The vet can fix Big Ben.

What can the vet do?
The vet can get a kit.

Big Ben can sit on the table.

The vet can get Big Ben wet.

Big Ben does not want to get wet.

My cat is wet and sad.
The vet can pat my cat.

Big Ben is not sad!
The vet can do a lot for my pet!

Chapter 2

My big pet is in a big pen.

Mom, get the vet!

Is the vet here yet?
I pat my sad, sad pet.

Here is the vet in a tan van!
The vet can fix my pet.

What can the vet do?
The vet can get a big kit.

My pet is not sad!

A vet can do a lot for a pet!

Think About the Story

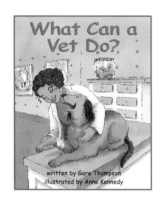

1 What does a vet do?

2 How do you know the girl and the boy care about their pets?

3 Would you like to be a vet? Why?

Write a Description

Draw a picture of a pet at the vet.
Write about your picture.

**Hot Fox
Soup**

Words to Know

do	kit
said	vat
my	yet
me	met
is	get
you	wet
I	Hen

Hen got a big kit.
Hen got a big vat.
Hen met Fox.

"What can I do?" said Fox.
"I can get you wet," said Hen.
"Here is my vat. Get in."
"Not me," said Fox.

"Get wet," said Hen.
"Not yet," said Fox.

Meet the Author
and Illustrator

Satoshi Kitamura

HOT FOX SOUP

by

SATOSHI KITAMURA

Fox wanted hot hen soup.

Fox got a big, big vat.
Fox lit a hot, hot fire.

Fox got a noodle soup kit.

Fox met Hen.
"What can I do?" said Hen.

"Get wet in my vat," said Fox.

196

"Not me!" said Hen.
"I do not want to be hen soup!"

Fox met Pig.
Fox wanted hot pig soup.

"What can I do?" said Pig.

"Get wet in my vat," said Fox.

"Not me!" said Pig.
"I do not want to be pig soup!"

Fox met Ox.
Fox wanted hot ox soup.

"What can I do?" said Ox.

"Get wet in my vat," said Fox.

"Not me!" said Ox.
"I can not fit in the vat."

Ox said, "You can fit, Fox.
We can get hot fox soup!"

"Not hot fox soup!" said Fox.
"We can have hot noodle soup."

"Is it hot yet?" said Ox.
"We want hot noodle soup."

"Me, too!" said Fox.

Think About the Story

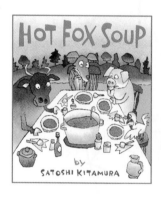

1 Why wouldn't the animals get in Fox's vat?

2 How did Ox surprise Fox?

3 Would you eat soup with Fox? Why?

![Writing](pencil icon)

Write a Sign

Make a sign with the words
Hot _____ *Soup.* Add your own
word to complete the sign.

Polly, Put

the Kettle On

Polly, put the kettle on,
Polly, put the kettle on,
Polly, put the kettle on,
We'll all have tea.

English Traditional Song

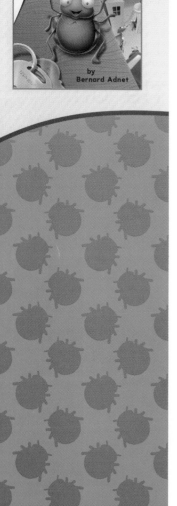

Words to Know

does	hut
he	jug
live	Bug
where	rug
quit	tug
Zig	

Where does Zig Bug live?

Does he live in a hut?

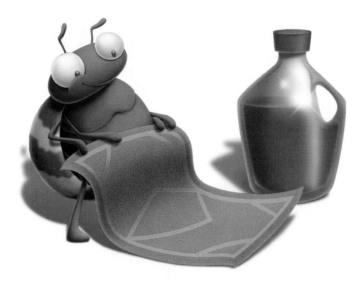

Zig Bug can get a jug.
Zig Bug can get a rug.

Do not quit, Zig Bug!
Tug, tug, tug!

Meet the Author and Illustrator
Bernard Adnet

A Hut for Zig Bug

by
Bernard Adnet

Does Zig Bug have a hut?
He does not.

Where can Zig Bug live?
Can Zig Bug live here?

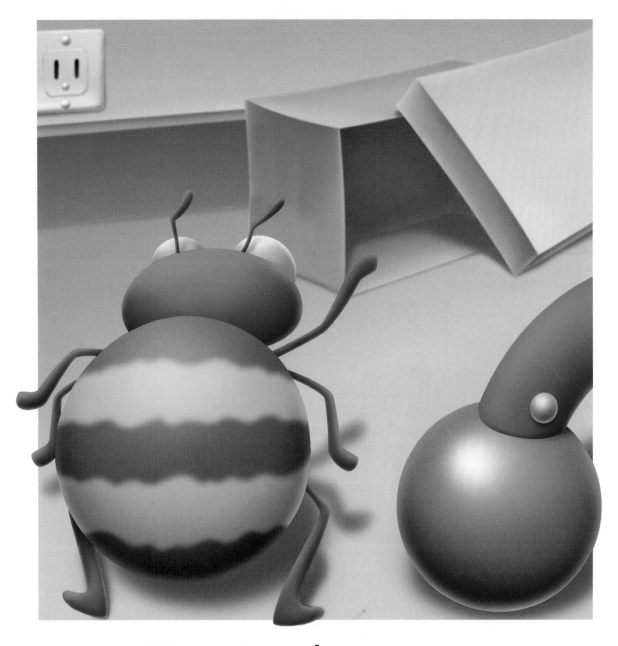

Here is a box.
Can a box be a hut?

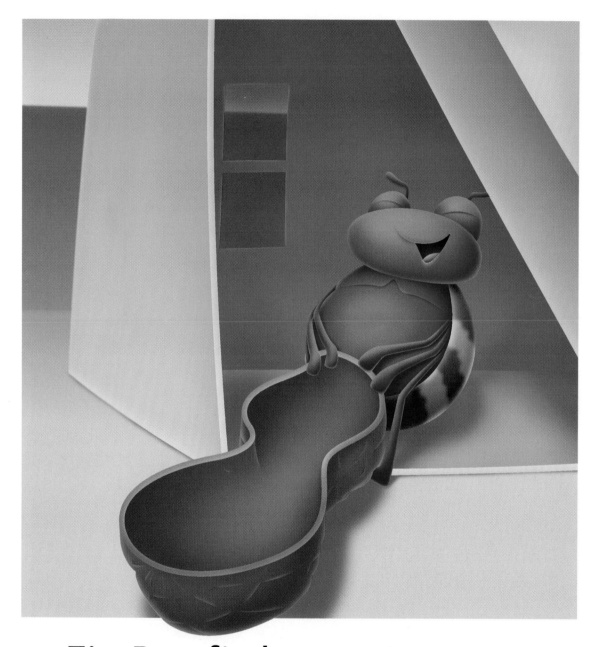

Zig Bug finds a cot!
Can he get the cot in the hut?

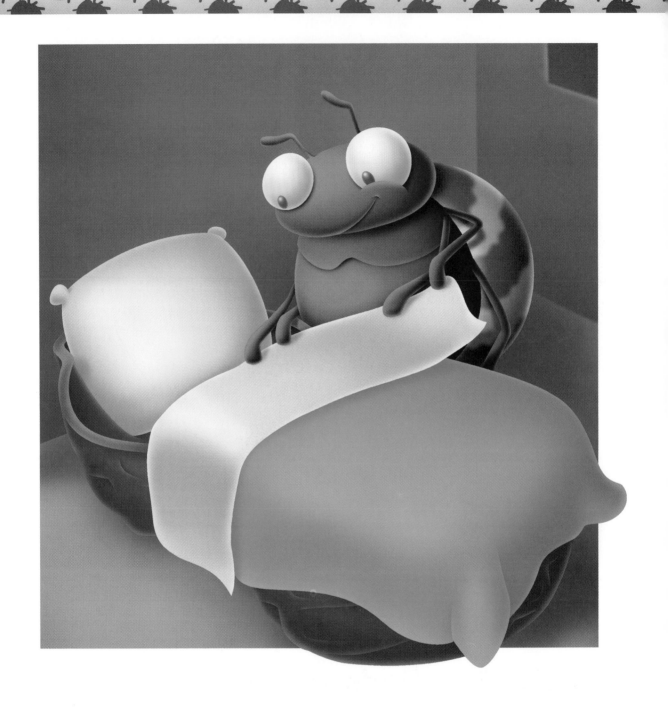

The little cot does fit in the hut.

Zig Bug finds a jug!
Can he get the jug in the hut?

The little jug does fit in the hut.
The hut has a cot and a jug.

Zig Bug finds a rug!
Can the rug fit in the hut?

The rug does fit in the hut.
Zig Bug has a cot, a jug,
and a rug.

Zig Bug finds a little pan.
Can he get the pan in the hut?

Zig Bug does get the pan in.
The hut has a cot, a jug, a rug,
and a pan.

Can Zig Bug fit in the hut?

Do not quit, Zig Bug!
You can fit!

The hut has a cot, a jug, a rug,
a pan, and Zig Bug!
Zig Bug can live in the hut.

Think About the Story

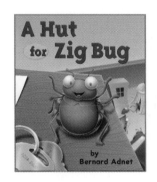

1 Was Zig Bug smart? Why?

2 What else could Zig Bug put in his hut?

3 Will Zig Bug be happy in his hut? Why?

232

Write a List

List the things Zig Bug put in his hut. Add some more things he could put in there.

The Rope
Tug

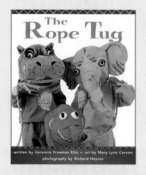

The
Rope Tug

written by Veronica Freeman Ellis • art by Mary Lynn Carson
photography by Richard Haynes

Words to Know

are	zig
does	jig
pull	hut
they	but
away	tug
quit	

Cat is in a big hut.
Can Rat pull Cat away?

"You are big," said Rat.
"But I can tug."
They tug, tug, tug.
Zig, zig, zig!

"I quit," said Cat.
The rat does a jig.

**Meet the Author
Veronica
Freeman Ellis**

**Meet the Artist
Mary Lynn
Carson**

**Meet the
Photographer
Richard Haynes**

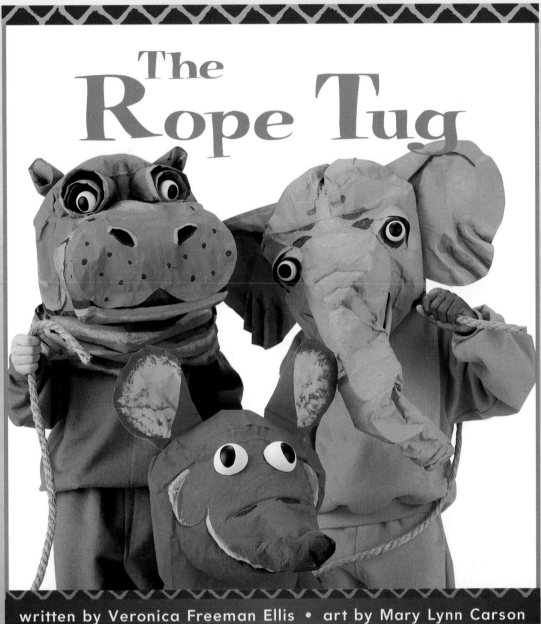

The Rope Tug

written by Veronica Freeman Ellis • art by Mary Lynn Carson

photography by Richard Haynes

Narrator

Elephant

Hippo

Rat

238

 Elephant can get in the hut.
Hippo can get in the hut, too.

Rat can not get in.
Rat does not fit.

 Let me in! Let me in!

You can not fit, Rat.
Go away! Go away!

 I will not go away!
I can pull you outside.
We can have a rope tug.

 You can not tug me, Rat.
I'm big and you are not!

A rat does not tug a hippo!

 Can you two pull me?
I'm not big, but I can tug.

 We can pull you!
Get a big rope, Rat!
We will win the rope tug!

 Rat finds a big rope.
Rat can do a lot with
the rope.

Rat can zig zag, zig zag.
Can Rat win the rope tug?

 Tug, tug, tug!

 We can tug and pull, Rat.
One, two, three, tug!

They are big!
They tug and tug and tug,
but they can not pull Rat.

 I quit!

 I quit!

 You win, Rat!

 I'm not big, but I can tug!

 Rat does a jig.

Think About the Story

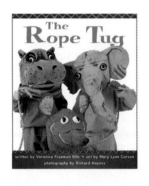

1 Why wouldn't Elephant and Hippo let Rat in the hut?

2 How did Rat surprise Elephant and Hippo?

3 How else could Rat have gotten Elephant and Hippo out of the hut?

252

Writing ▶

Write a Description

Draw your favorite part of the play.
Write some words to tell about it.

Way Down South

Way down South where
bananas grow,
A grasshopper stepped on
an elephant's toe.
The elephant said, with tears
in his eyes,
"Pick on somebody your
own size."

Anonymous

254

Acknowledgments

For each of the selections listed below, grateful acknowledgment is made for permission to excerpt and/or reprint original or copyrighted material, as follows:

Poetry

"At Night" from *Out in the Dark and Daylight,* by Aileen Fisher. Copyright © 1980 by Aileen Fisher. Used by permission of Marian Reiner for the author.

"Cats" by Jacquiline Kirk. Copyright © by Jacquiline Kirk. Reprinted by permission of the author.

"Here Is the Beehive" from *Hand Rhymes,* collected and illustrated by Marc Brown. Copyright © 1985 by Marc Brown. Published by Dutton Children's Books, a division of Penguin Putnam Inc.

"Riddle" from *The Llama Who Had No Pajama: 100 Favorite Poems,* by Mary Ann Hoberman. Copyright © 1973 by Mary Ann Hoberman. Reprinted by permission of Harcourt Inc.

"There was a small pig who wept tears . . ." from *The Book of Pigericks: Pig Limericks,* by Arnold Lobel. Copyright © 1983 by Arnold Lobel. Reprinted by permission of HarperCollins Publishers.

"Together" from *Embrace: Selected Love Poems,* by Paul Engle. Copyright © 1969 by Paul Engle. Reprinted by permission of Random House, Inc.

Credits

Photography

3 (t) image Copyright © 2000 PhotoDisc, Inc. **7** (t) image Copyright © 2000 PhotoDisc, Inc. **12** (icon) image Copyright © 2000 PhotoDisc, Inc. **12–13** Jo Browne/Mick Samee/Tony Stone Images. **16** Courtesy Lynn Munsinger. **27** (cat) Artville. **30** Courtesy NB Westcott. **44** Artville. **46–7** Artville. **50** Courtesy Lisa Campbell Ernst. **64** (l) American Images Inc./FPG International. (r) Jeri Gleiter/FPG International. **68** (t) Lawrence Migdale. (b) Mark Gardner. **82** images Copyright © 2000 PhotoDisc, Inc. **84–5** Telegraph Colour Library/FPG International. **88** Andrew Yates/Mercury Pictures. **89** Dennis Gray/Mercury Pictures. **104** images Copyright © 2000 PhotoDisc, Inc. **108** Sharron McElmeel. **124** images Copyright © 2000 PhotoDisc, Inc. **125** (r) image Copyright © 2000 PhotoDisc, Inc. **128** (icon) image Copyright © 2000 PhotoDisc, Inc. **128–9** Mauritius/Nawrocki Stock Photo Inc. **132** (t) Jon Crispin/Mercury Pictures. (b) Courtesy Cynthia Jabar. **150** Courtesy Valeria Petrone. **170** (t) Kindra Clineff. (b) Courtesy Anne Kennedy. **186** image Copyright © 2000 PhotoDisc, Inc. **190** Courtesy Farrar, Straus and Giroux. **210** image Copyright © 2000 PhotoDisc, Inc. **216** Courtesy Bernard Adnet. **236** (t) Jesse Nemerofksy/Mercury Pictures.

Assignment Photography

66–67, 69–81 Joel Benjamin; **26–7, 45, 65, 83, 105, 125** (l), **146–7, 164–5, 166–7, 187, 211, 232–3, 253** David Bradley Photographer; **236** (m&b) **234–5, 237–252** Richard Haynes.

Illustration

14–25 Lynn Munsinger. **28–43** Nadine Wescott. **48–63** Lisa Campbell Ernst. **70–81(t)** Rob Dunlavey. **86–103** John Ceballos. **106–123** David McPhail. **126–127** Stef De Reuver. **130–145** Cynthia Jabar. **148–163** Valerie Petrone. **166–167** Tammy Smith. **168–185** Anne Kennedy. **188–209** Satoshi Kitamura. **212–213** Matt Novak. **214–231** Bernard Adnet. **234–251** Mary Lynn Carson. **254–255** Keiko Motoyama.